Cole Porter

Music arranged and processed by Barnes Music Engraving Ltd
East Sussex TN22 4HA, UK

Cover design by xheight Limited

Published 1995

© International Music Publications Limited
Southend Road, Woodford Green, Essex IG8 8HN, England

BEGIN THE BEGUINE

Words and Music by
COLE PORTER

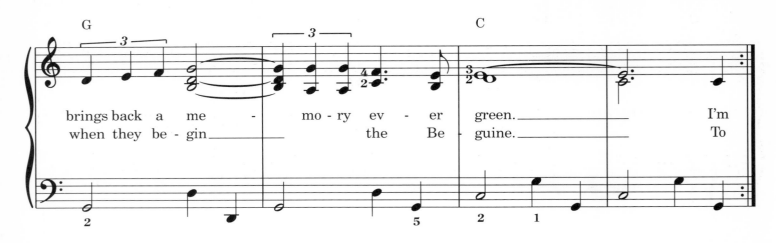

brings back a me - mo - ry ev - er green._____ I'm
when they be - gin_____ the Be - guine._____ To

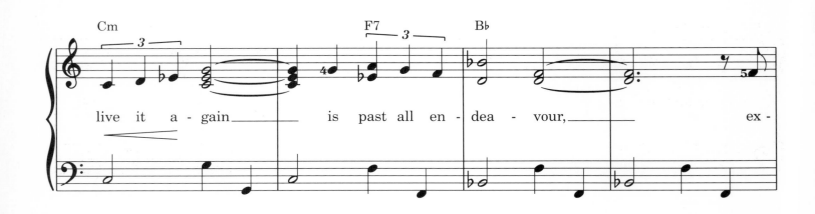

live it a - gain_____ is past all en - dea - vour,_____ ex -

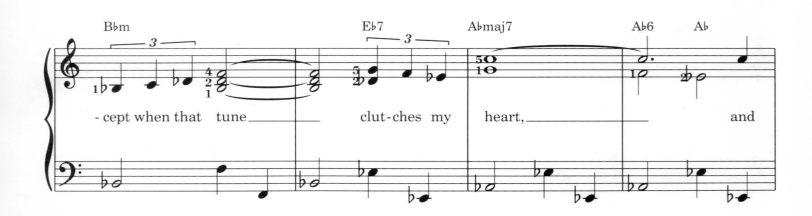

- cept when that tune_____ clut-ches my heart,_____ and

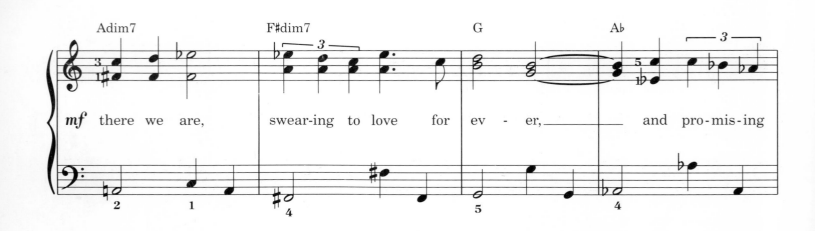

there we are, swear-ing to love for ev - er,_____ and pro-mis-ing

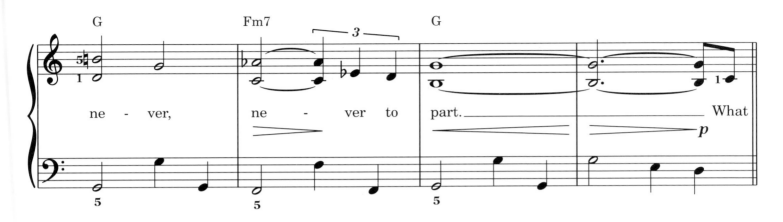

ne - ver, ne - ver to part._____ What

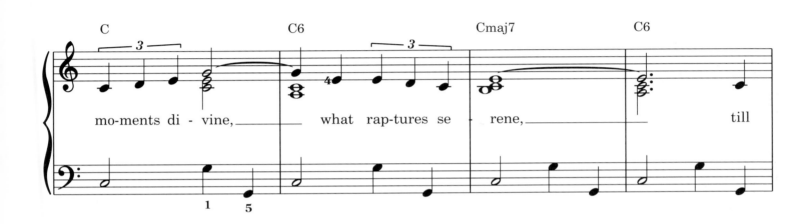

mo-ments di - vine,_____ what rap-tures se - rene,_____ till

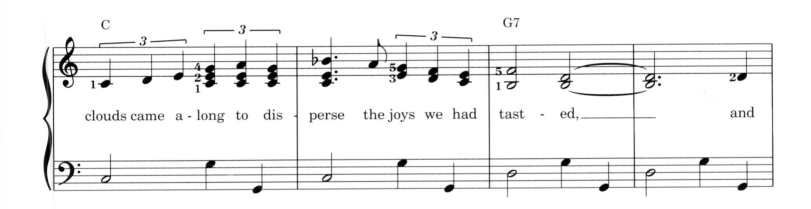

clouds came a - long to dis - perse the joys we had tast - ed,_____ and

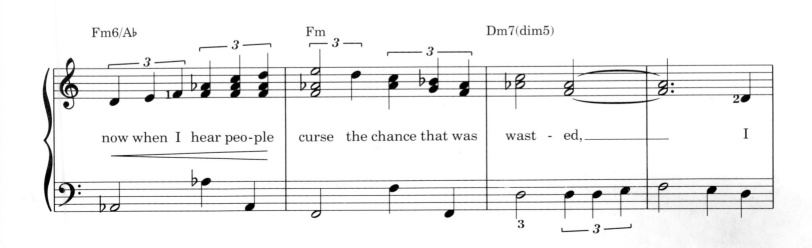

now when I hear peo-ple curse the chance that was wast - ed,_____ I

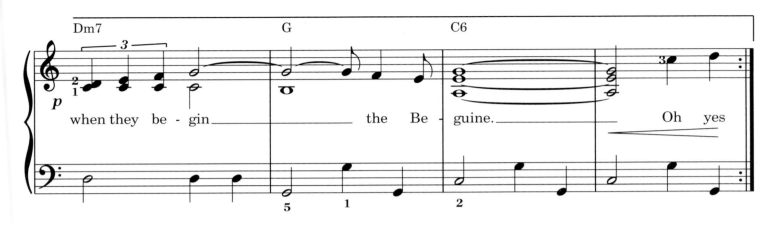

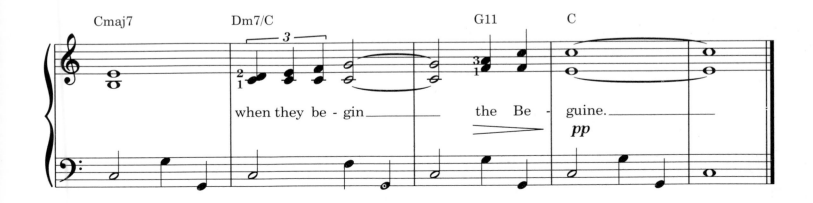

ALL OF YOU

Words and Music by
COLE PORTER

I love the looks of you, the lure of

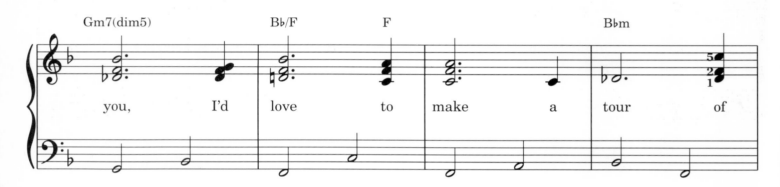

you, I'd love to make a tour of

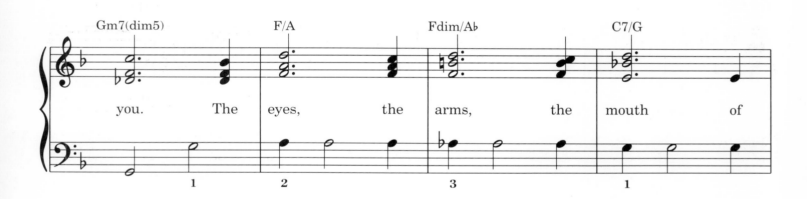

you. The eyes, the arms, the mouth of

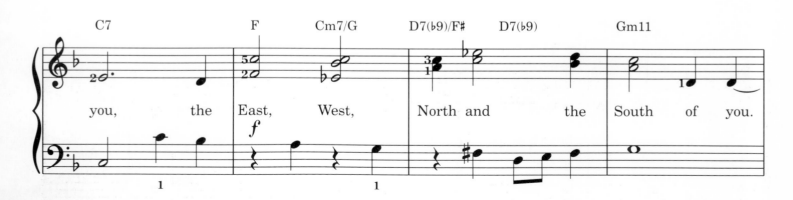

you, the East, West, North and the South of you.

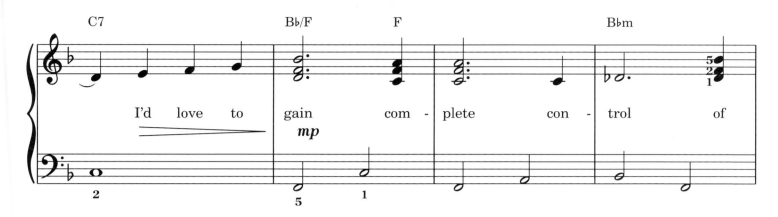

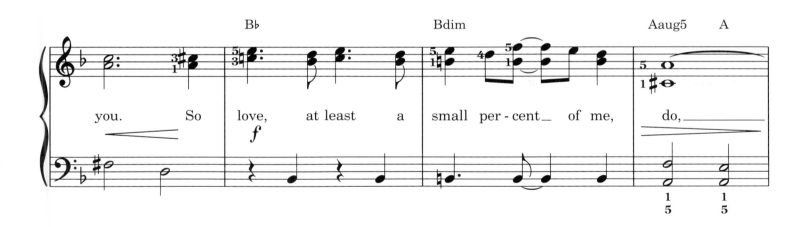

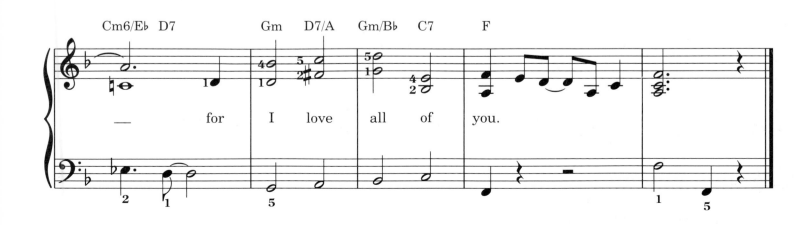

C'EST MAGNIFIQUE

Words and Music by
COLE PORTER

Allegro

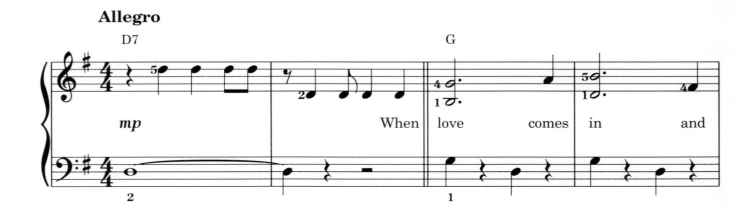

EASY TO LOVE

Words and Music by
COLE PORTER

13

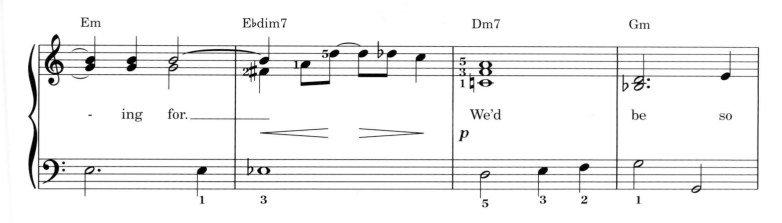

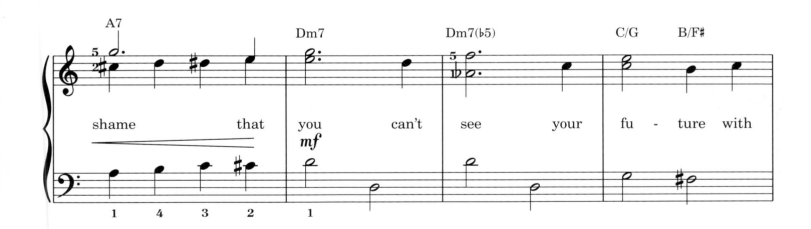

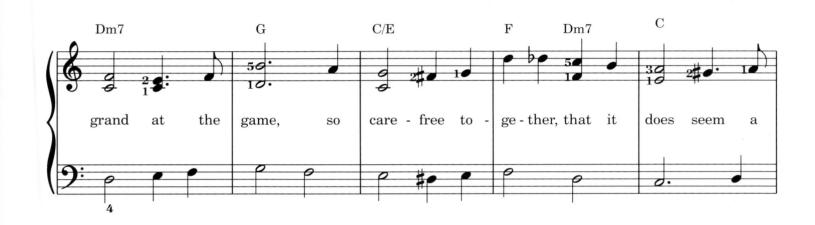

EV'RY TIME WE SAY GOODBYE

Words and Music by
COLE PORTER

I LOVE PARIS

Words and Music by
COLE PORTER

I'VE GOT YOU UNDER MY SKIN

Words and Music by
COLE PORTER

Allegro sostenuto

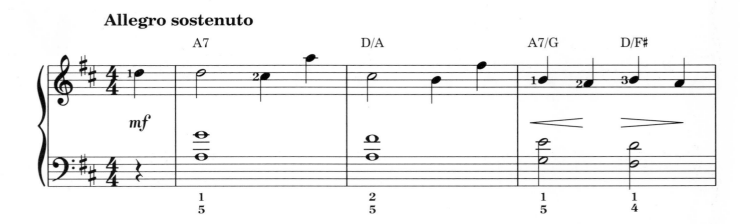

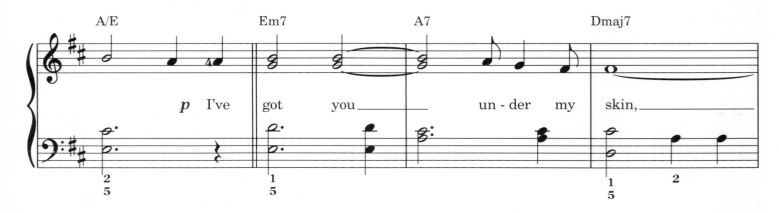

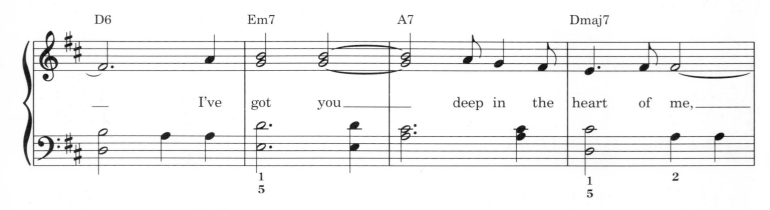

20

I GET A KICK OUT OF YOU

Words and Music by
COLE PORTER

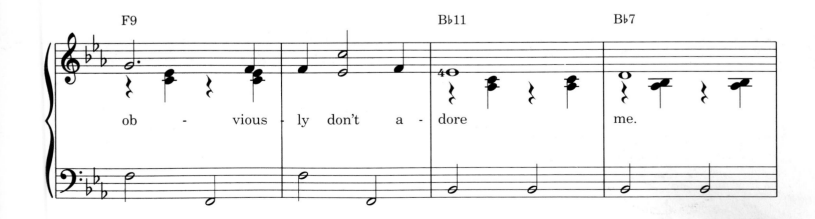

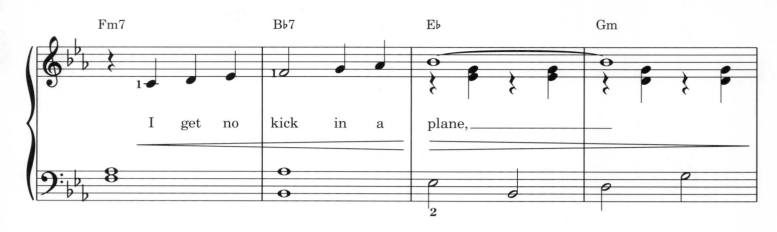

I get no kick in a plane,_____

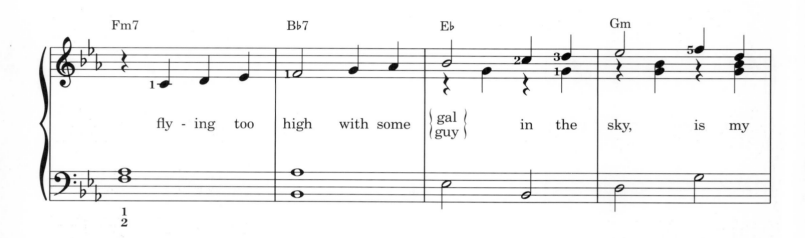

fly - ing too high with some {gal / guy} in the sky, is my

i - dea of no - thing to do,_____ yet

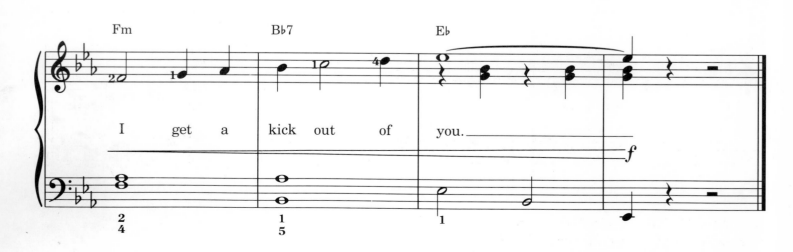

I get a kick out of you._____

IT'S ALL RIGHT WITH ME

Words and Music by
COLE PORTER

IT'S DE-LOVELY

Words and Music by
COLE PORTER

Allegretto

The night is young, the skies are clear and if you want to go

walk-ing dear, it's de - light - ful, __ it's de - li - cious, it's de - love - ly. __

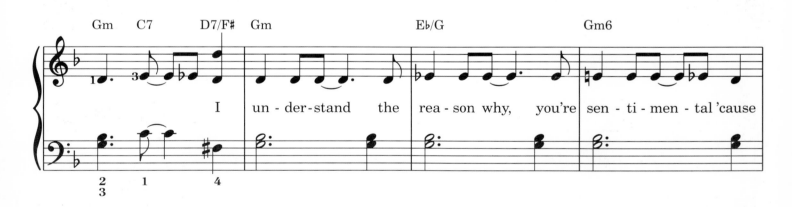

I un-der-stand the rea - son why, you're sen - ti - men - tal 'cause

so am I, __ it's de - light - ful, __ it's de - li - cious, it's de - love - ly. __

LET'S DO IT
(Let's Fall In Love)

Words and Music by
COLE PORTER

Moderato

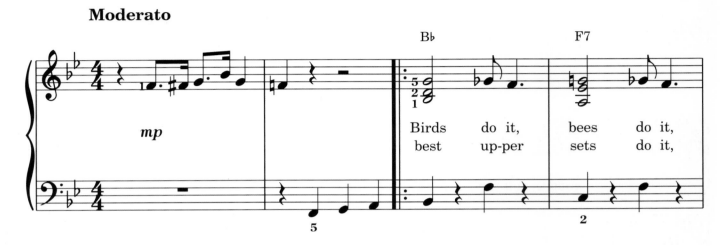

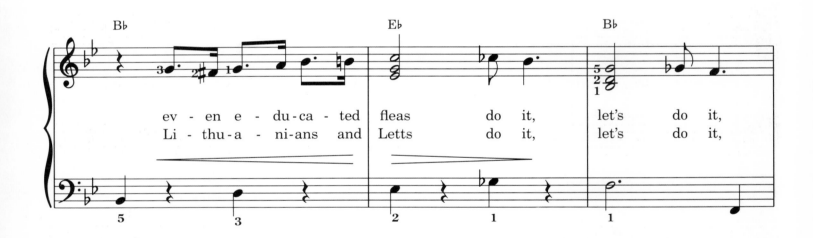

LOVE FOR SALE

Words and Music by
COLE PORTER

Moderato

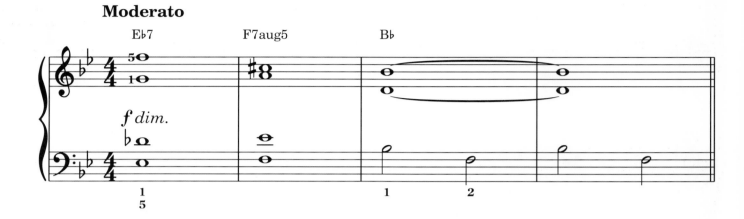

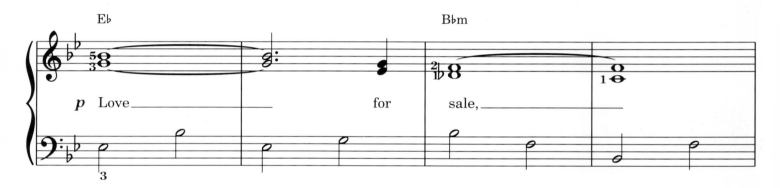

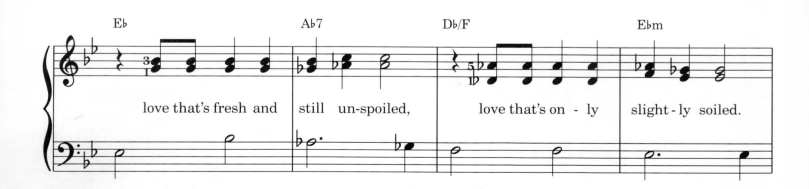

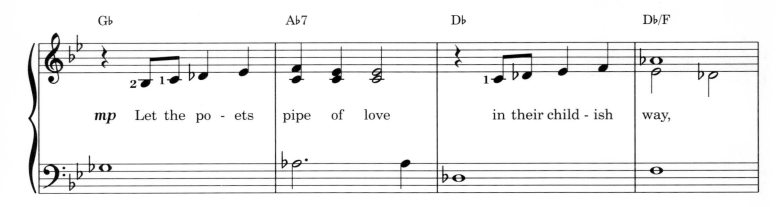

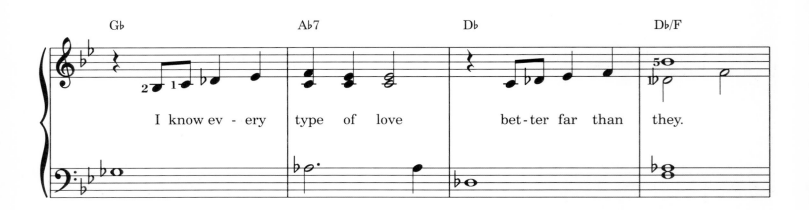

a tempo

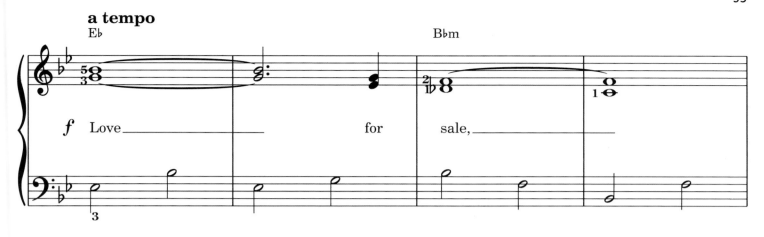

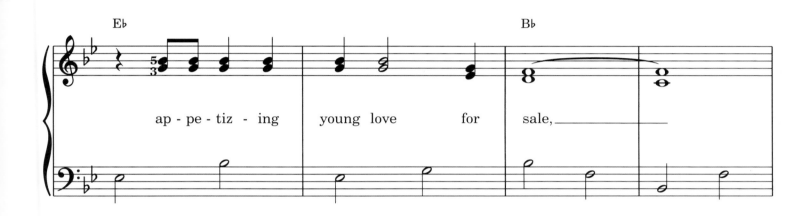

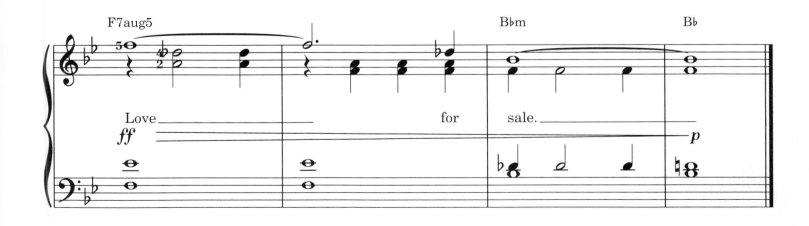

NIGHT AND DAY

Words and Music by
COLE PORTER

Moderato

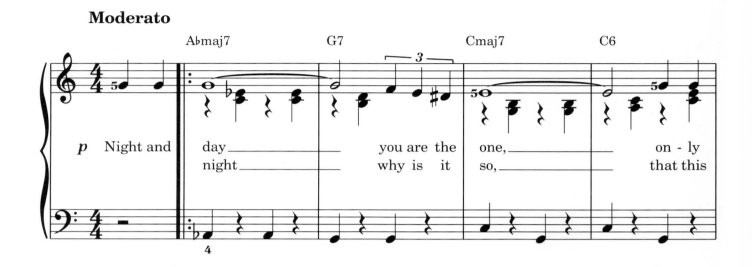

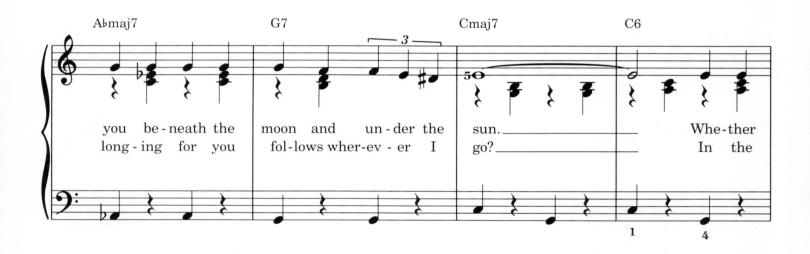

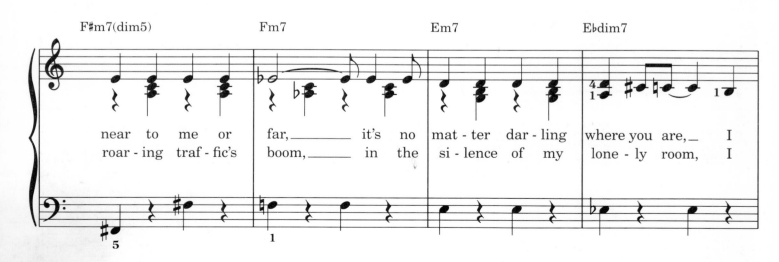

WHAT IS THIS THING CALLED LOVE?

Words and Music by
COLE PORTER

YOU DO SOMETHING TO ME

Words and Music by
COLE PORTER

YOU'RE THE TOP

Words and Music by
COLE PORTER

Take it easy

IRVING BERLIN

Blue Skies
Cheek To Cheek
A Couple Of Swells
Easter Parade
How Deep Is The Ocean (How High Is The Sky)
I'm Putting All My Eggs In One Basket
Let's Face The Music And Dance
Play A Simple Melody

Puttin' On The Ritz
Sisters
Steppin' Out With My Baby
There's No Business Like Show Business
Top Hat, White Tie And Tails
What'll I Do
When I Leave The World Behind
White Christmas

GEORGE GERSHWIN AND IRA GERSHWIN

But Not For Me
Embraceable You
Funny Face
How Long Has This Been Going On?
I Got Plenty O' Nuttin'
I Got Rhythm
It Ain't Necessarily So
I've Got A Crush On You

Liza (All The Clouds'll Roll Away)
The Man I Love
My One And Only (What Am I Gonna Do)
Oh, Lady Be Good!
Rhapsody In Blue
Strike Up The Band
Summertime
'S Wonderful

SCOTT JOPLIN

The Easy Winners
Elite Syncopations
The Entertainer
Maple Leaf Rag
Palm Leaf Rag
Paragon Rag
Peacherine Rag
Weeping Willow

Pine Apple Rag
Rag-Time Dance
Reflection Rag (Syncopated Musings)
Scott Joplin's New Rag
Something Doing
Sunflower Slow Drag
Swipesy (Cake Walk)

COLE PORTER

All Of You
Begin The Beguine
C'est Magnifique
Easy To Love
Ev'ry Time We Say Goodbye
I Get A Kick Out Of You
I Love Paris
I've Got You Under My Skin

It's All Right With Me
It's De-Lovely
Let's Do It (Let's Fall In Love)
Love For Sale
Night And Day
What Is This Thing Called Love?
You Do Something To Me
You're The Top

NOVELTY SONGS

Anything You Can Do
The Bee Song
Combine Harvester (Brand New Key)
Flash, Bang, Wallop!
The Flies Crawled Up The Window
I've Never Seen A Straight Banana
Itsy Bitsy Teenie Weenie Yellow Polka Dot Bikini
Mairzy Doats and Dozy Doats
The Marrow Song (Oh! What A Beauty)

The Mole In The Hole
Nola
The Pink Panther
The Prune Song (No Matter How Young A Prune
   May Be It's Always Full Of Wrinkles)
The Purple People Eater
There's A Worm At The Bottom Of The Garden
Yakety Yak
Yes! We Have No Bananas